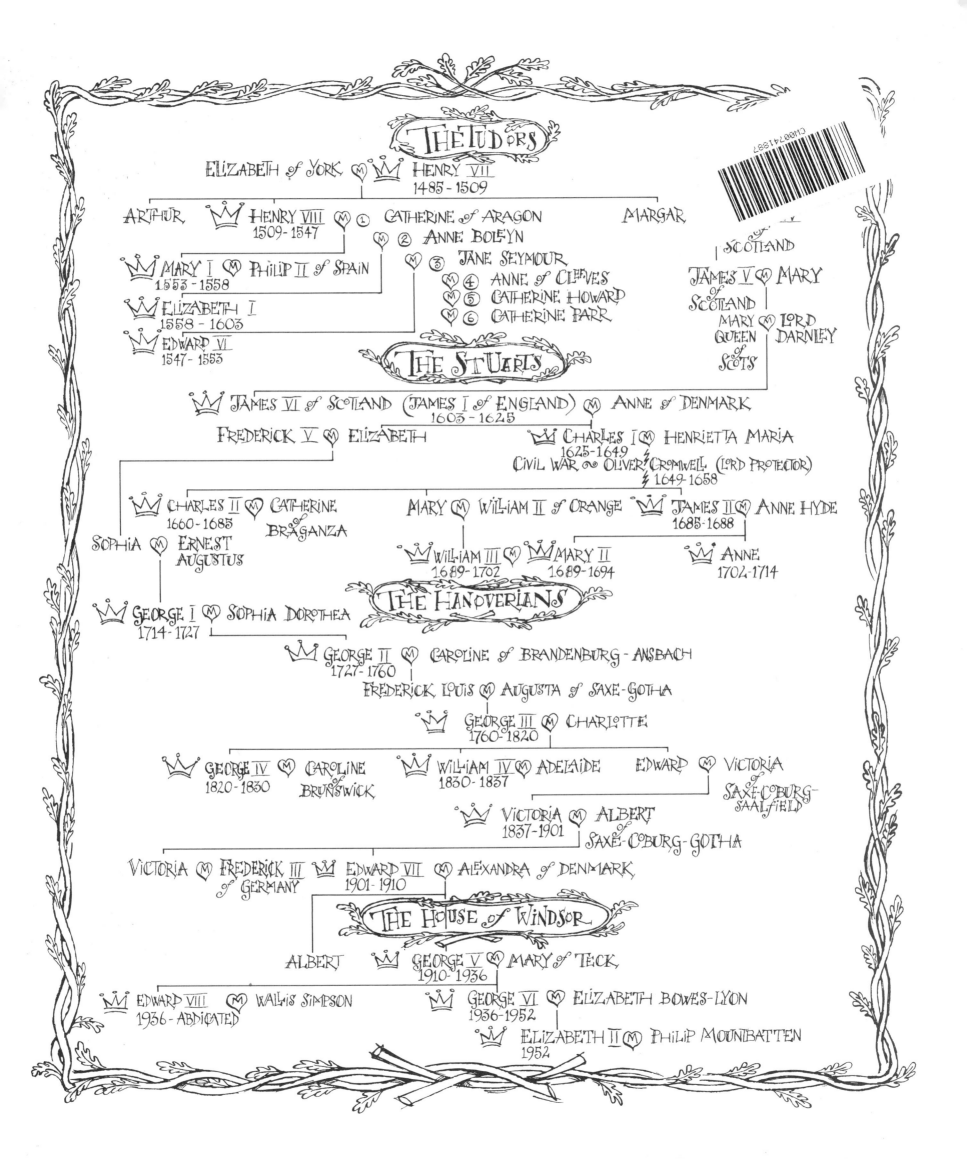

Kings & Queens of Britain

A Victorian Mnemonic or Learning Verse Compiled & Illustrated by:-

Rowan Barnes-Murphy

Captions Researched & Written by:-

Frances Barnes-Murphy

HO SO Y PENSE

DIEU ET MON DROIT

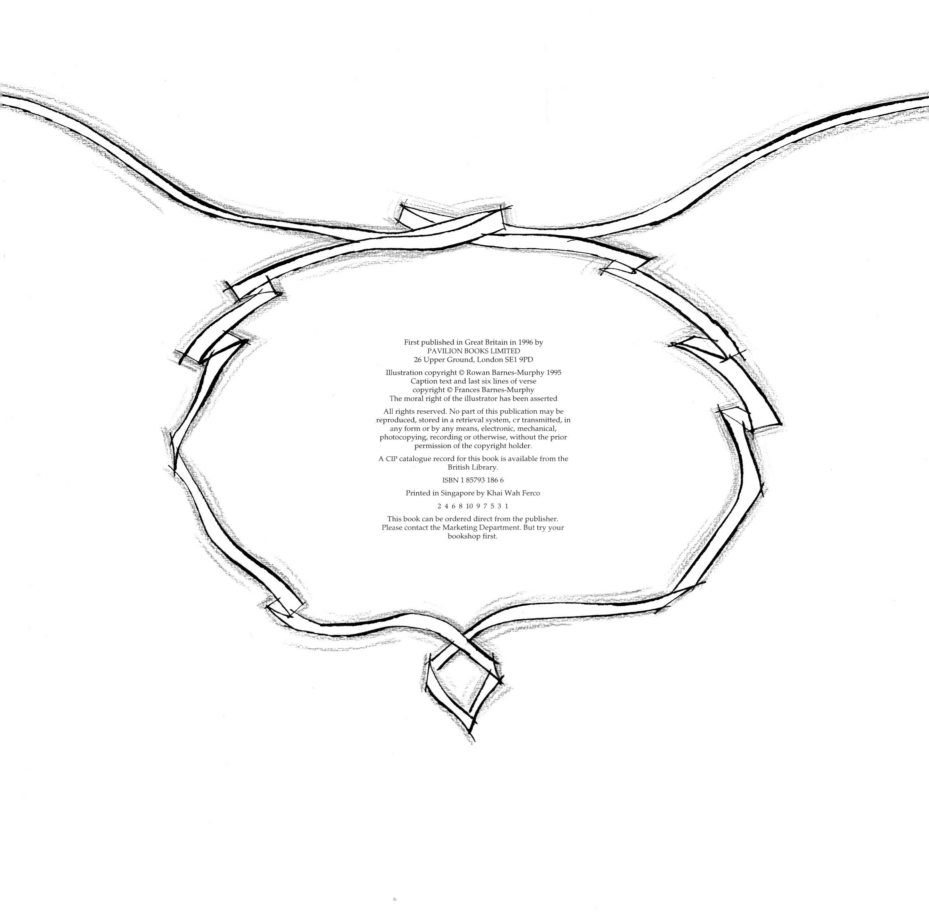

First published in Great Britain in 1996 by
PAVILION BOOKS LIMITED
26 Upper Ground, London SE1 9PD

Illustration copyright © Rowan Barnes-Murphy 1995
Caption text and last six lines of verse
copyright © Frances Barnes-Murphy
The moral right of the illustrator has been asserted

A CIP catalogue record for this book is available from the
British Library.

ISBN 1 85793 186 6

Printed in Singapore by Khai Wah Ferco

2 4 6 8 10 9 7 5 3 1

This book can be ordered direct from the publisher.
Please contact the Marketing Department. But try your
bookshop first.

Kings & Queens of Britain

William the Conqueror, long did reign
William Rufus by an arrow was slain
Henry I was a scholar, bright
Stephen was King without any right
Henry II Plantagenet's scion
Richard I was as brave as a lion
John though a tyrant the charter, signed
Henry III had a weakly mind
Edward I conquered Cumbria's dales
Edward II was crowned Prince of Wales
Edward III restored Scotia's pride
Richard II by Henry's hand died
Henry IV then wore the crown
Henry V pulled the French king down
Henry VI lost the Roses & France
Edward IV led the Commons a dance
Edward V was slain with his brother
Richard III soon gave way to another
Henry VII was frugal of means
Henry VIII had too many Queens
Edward VI Reformation began

Bloody Mary frustrated the plan
Wise & profound were Elizabeth's ways
England & Scotland were joined under James
Charles found the people a cruel corrector
Oliver Cromwell became Lord Protector
Charles II hid in an oak
James II took Popery's yoke
William & Mary next shared the throne
Good Queen Anne then reigned alone
George I from Hanover came
George II carried on the name
George III was loved in the land
George IV was pompous & grand
William IV had no heir, of his own
So good Queen Victoria came to the throne
Edward VII loved gambling & fun
George V reigned through World War One
Edward VIII gave his throne for a wife
George VI saw more World War strife
Elizabeth II was crowned young & serene
And the people still sing 'God Save our Queen'

This verse, called a mnemonic, was written in Victorian times to help people remember the order of the Kings and Queens of Britain. The original verse finished with Queen Victoria, so we have added the last six lines to bring the mnemonic up to date.

Illustrated by:
Rowan Barnes-Murphy

Lettering & Captions by:
Frances Barnes-Murphy

WILLIAM THE CONQUEROR LONG DID REIGN

KNOWN AS WILLIAM THE **BASTARD** HE WAS A NORTHMAN OR NORMAN

THE NORMANS RULED FOR 88 YEARS

WILLIAM'S ARMY DEFEATED THE SAXONS AT THE **BATTLE of HASTINGS 1066.**

THE **BAYEUX TAPESTRY** (REALLY AN EMBROIDERY) OVER **70 METRES** LONG IS A RECORD OF HAROLD'S LIFE AND FEATURES THE NORMAN INVASION OF BRITAIN.

WILLIAM DIED OF HIS INJURIES AFTER FALLING FROM HIS HORSE WHILE FIGHTING IN NORMANDY, FRANCE

HAROLD SAT HERE

THE **DOMESDAY BOOK** RECORDED WHO OWNED AND FARMED THE LAND AND WHAT EACH PROPERTY WAS WORTH SO WILLIAM KNEW EXACTLY HOW MUCH HIS SUBJECTS COULD PAY TOWARDS WAR.

IN 1086 WILLIAM HAD THE **DOMESDAY BOOK** COMPILED.

FEW PEOPLE COULD READ OR WRITE.

BEWARE OF THE BEARS

SAXON VILLAGES AND ANCIENT FORESTS WERE DESTROYED IN SOUTHERN ENGLAND TO CREATE THE NEW FOREST (A ROYAL HUNTING GROUND). COMMONERS WERE PROHIBITED FROM KILLING RED DEER, WILD BOAR, OR SETTING TRAPS FOR SMALL ANIMALS, NOR COULD THEY ENTICE ANIMALS BY MUSIC!

SIXTY

BORN 1028 AND CROWNED ON CHRISTMAS DAY SUCCEEDED 1066 MARRIED **MATILDA of FLANDERS** DIED **1087** BURIED AT CAEN IN NORMANDY

WILLIAM RUFUS BY an ARROW WAS SLAIN

SIR WALTER TYRELL

HENRY (BROTHER of RUFUS)

WILLIAM II WAS KNOWN AS WILLIAM RUFUS BECAUSE OF HIS RED HAIR AND COMPLEXION.

HAWKS WERE TRAINED TO HUNT HERON & WILD GEESE.

RUFUS DIED IN MYSTERIOUS CIRCUMSTANCES FROM AN ARROW WOUND WHILST HUNTING IN THE NEW FOREST. THE ARROW WAS SUPPOSEDLY FIRED BY THE KING'S FRIEND, WALTER TYRELL, BUT IT MAY HAVE BEEN THE KING'S BROTHER, HENRY, WHO KILLED HIM DELIBERATELY.

THE RUFUS STONE IN THE NEW FOREST MARKS THE SPOT WHERE RUFUS DIED.

LONG HAIR BECAME FASHIONABLE FOR MEN. THEY WORE SHOES WITH LONG TOES STUFFED WITH WOOL TO KEEP THEIR SHAPE.

WOMEN'S FASHION
DRESSES HAD SLEEVES SO WIDE THAT THEY WERE KNOTTED TO STOP THEM TRAILING ON THE GROUND.

SOME MEN WORE SKIRTS AND SUCH TIGHT-FITTING TUNICS THAT THEY WALKED WITH A MINCING GAIT!

RUFUS IS BURIED UNDER THE FLAGSTONES IN WINCHESTER CATHEDRAL.

BORN 1057
SUCCEEDED 1087
WILLIAM NEVER MARRIED
DIED 1100 BURIED IN WINCHESTER CATHEDRAL

HENRY I WAS A SCHOLAR BRIGHT

HENRY'S SON & HEIR, WILLIAM, DROWNED WHEN HIS SHIP SANK IN 1120.

HENRY WAS KNOWN AS 'BEAUCLERC' BECAUSE HE COULD READ AND WRITE FLUENTY IN BOTH LATIN & ENGLISH.

HENRY IMPRISONED HIS BROTHER, ROBERT, IN CORFE CASTLE, DORSET, FOR 28 YEARS.

HENRY DIED IN NORMANDY FROM EATING TOO MANY LAMPREYS (EEL-LIKE CREATURES).

A CHEQUERED TABLE CLOTH WAS USED TO HELP CALCULATE TAXES. THE MODERN EXCHEQUER REFERS TO THIS ANCIENT SYSTEM.

HENRY KEPT A POLAR BEAR AND OTHER WILD ANIMALS IN THE TOWER OF LONDON.

BORN 1068   SUCCEEDED 1100
MARRIED MATILDA & ADELA
DIED 1135 BURIED IN READING ABBEY

STEPHEN WAS A KING WITHOUT ANY RIGHT

STEPHEN DIED OF DYSENTERY, INTESTINAL OBSTRUCTION & HAEMORRHOIDS IN THE CITY OF CANTERBURY.

STEPHEN PROMISED HIS UNCLE, HENRY I, THAT HE WOULD ACCEPT MATILDA, HENRY'S DAUGHTER, AS QUEEN. BUT WHEN HENRY DIED STEPHEN SNATCHED THE THRONE FROM MATILDA. SHE REGAINED IT SIX YEARS LATER AND IMPRISONED HIM!

STEPHEN WAS NOT A STRONG KING. HIS BARONS SENSED THIS AND ANARCHY AND CIVIL WAR ENSUED. VILLAGES WERE DESTROYED, FARMS BURNED AND CROPS LEFT TO ROT. THOUSANDS OF PEOPLE STARVED.

MATILDA (HENRY'S DAUGHTER AND HEIR)

BORN 1097   SUCCEEDED 1135
MARRIED MATILDA OF BOULOGNE
DIED 1154 BURIED IN FAVERSHAM ABBEY

HENRY II PLANTAGENET'S SCION

HENRY WAS KNOWN AS FITZ-EMPRESS AND NICKNAMED CURTMANTEL BECAUSE HE FAVOURED SHORT CLOAKS INSTEAD OF LONG DUSTY ONES WORN BY MOST NOBLEMEN.

THE LEGAL SYSTEM WAS CHANGED SO THAT TRIALS HAD TO BE HEARD IN COURT.

ATHLETIC AND ENERGETIC, HENRY LIKED TO VAULT OVER TABLES INSTEAD OF WALKING AROUND THEM.

ELEANOR of AQUITAINE

PREVIOUSLY MARRIED TO LOUIS VII OF FRANCE, SHE & HENRY HAD SEVEN SURVIVING CHILDREN BUT THEIR MARRIAGE WAS STORMY.

SHE HELPED HER SONS TO REBEL AGAINST HENRY SO WAS IMPRISONED BY HIM AND HELD CAPTIVE FOR OVER 15 YEARS.

HENRY WAS THE FIRST PLANTAGENET. THE NAME PLANTAGENET DERIVED FROM 'PLANTA GENISTA' (BROOM) THE EMBLEM OF HENRY'S FATHER GEOFFREY OF ANJOU.

NICHOLAS BREAKSPEAR BECAME POPE ADRIAN IV - THE ONLY BRITISH POPE.

HENRY II CREATED HIS GOOD FRIEND THOMAS BECKET ARCHBISHOP OF CANTERBURY IN 1162 BUT THEY QUARRELLED OVER HOW MUCH POWER THE CHURCH SHOULD HAVE, FORCING THE KING TO UTTER THE FAMOUS WORDS 'WILL NOT SOMEONE RID ME OF THIS TURBULENT PRIEST?'

THOMAS BECKET

FOUR KNIGHTS TOOK THE KING AT HIS WORD AND MURDERED THOMAS BECKET IN CANTERBURY CATHEDRAL IN 1170.

BORN 1133   SUCCEEDED 1154
MARRIED ELEANOR DUCHESS of AQUITAINE
DIED 1189 BURIED AT FONTEVRAULT ABBEY

RICHARD I WAS AS BRAVE AS A LION

RICHARD WAS KNOWN AS 'COEUR DE LION', LIONHEARTED. HE MARRIED BERENGARIA of NAVARRE IN CYPRUS. RICHARD LOVED WARFARE & SPENT MOST of HIS REIGN FIGHTING ABROAD. ALTHOUGH HE ONLY SPENT 6 MONTHS IN ENGLAND, HE WAS REGARDED BY HIS SUBJECTS AS A HERO

RICHARD NEVER SPOKE THE ENGLISH LANGUAGE.

CHAIN MAIL ARMOUR

A COIF WITH EXTRA CHIN PIECE

THE POPE ORDERED ALL CHRISTIANS TO FIGHT CRUSADES TO RECAPTURE THE HOLY LANDS FROM THE TURKS. RICHARD LED THE THIRD CRUSADE (1189-92) WITH PHILIP II of FRANCE & DEFEATED THE SULTAN, SALADIN.

EVEN MITTENS WERE MADE IN CHAIN MAIL. LEGS WERE PROTECTED BY GAITERS.

A CRUSADER

A SARACEN OR TURKISH WARRIOR

FLIGHTS

A CROSSBOW MAN

A CROSSBOW BOLT OR QUARREL. THE FLIGHTS WERE MADE of WOOD OR LEATHER.

KING RICHARD DIED AGE 41 IN CHALUS, LIMOUSIN, of GANGRENE FROM A CROSSBOW BOLT WOUND. HIS BODY WAS BURIED AT FONTEVRAULT, HIS HEART AT ROUEN & HIS BRAIN AT ANJOU.

A MONASTIC ORDER, THE KNIGHTS TEMPLAR, WAS FOUNDED IN 1118 TO PROTECT PILGRIMS ON THEIR WAY TO JERUSALEM. THEY BUILT THIS CHURCH (PICTURED) IN CAMBRIDGE.

BORN 1157   SUCCEEDED 1189
MARRIED BERENGARIA of NAVARRE IN CYPRUS. DIED IN 1199 IN FRANCE
BURIED (MOSTLY) AT FONTEVRAULT

JOHN THOUGH A TYRANT

THE CHARTER SIGNED

JOHN WAS KNOWN AS 'LACKLAND' BECAUSE, AS THE YOUNGEST OF THE FAMILY, HE WOULD INHERIT NO LANDS.

THE KING MARRIED HIS SECOND WIFE, ISABELLA OF ANGOULÊME, WHEN SHE WAS TWELVE YEARS OLD!

IN 1215 JOHN WAS FORCED TO SIGN THE MAGNA CARTA (GREAT CHARTER) AT RUNNYMEDE BY ANGRY BARONS UPSET AT HAVING TO PAY HIGH TAXES.

JOHN LITERALLY LOST HIS CROWN & HIS JEWELS WHEN THEY SANK WITH HIS SHIP IN THE WASH (THE SEA BETWEEN LINCOLNSHIRE AND NORFOLK).

JOHN WAS EXCOMMUNICATED FROM THE CATHOLIC CHURCH OVER A CLASH WITH THE POPE ABOUT THE CHOICE OF THE NEW ARCHBISHOP OF CANTERBURY.

HUBERT DE BURGH

WILLIAM MARSHAL

ARCHBISHOP LANGTON

THESE THREE MEN ADVISED THE KING TO SIGN THE MAGNA CARTA TO AVOID CIVIL WAR

CORFE CASTLE IN DORSET WAS ONE OF JOHN'S FAVOURITE HOMES & HE CARRIED OUT BUILDING WORK THERE. HE IMPRISONED 22 FRENCH KNIGHTS WITHIN THE CASTLE AND STARVED THEM TO DEATH.

BORN 1167 SUCCEEDED 1199 MARRIED HADWISA (ISABELLA) OF GLOUCESTER & ISABELLA OF ANGOULÊME DIED 1216 BURIED IN WORCESTER CATHEDRAL

HENRY III HAD A WEAKLY MIND

EDWARD I CONQUERED CUMBRIA'S DALES

Henry did not really have a weak mind, although he was a weak king. He became senile in his old age.

In 1264 Simon de Montfort, Henry's brother-in-law, asked knights & representatives of certain towns to attend a meeting. It was called a 'Parliament', derived from the French word 'parler', to speak.

This was the golden age of church architecture. Wells & Lincoln cathedrals were built and work started on Salisbury cathedral.

OXFORD UNIVERSITY WAS FOUNDED IN 1214

BORN 1207 SUCCEEDED 1216 MARRIED ELEANOR OF PROVENCE DIED 1272 BURIED IN WESTMINSTER ABBEY

ELEANOR OF CASTILE

MARGARET OF FRANCE

EDWARD MARRIED HIS FIRST WIFE WHEN SHE WAS 10. HE WAS 15!

SALVINO DEGLI ARMATI (1245-1317) IS BELIEVED TO BE THE INVENTOR OF SPECTACLES.

HE MARRIED HIS SECOND WIFE WHEN SHE WAS 17 & HE WAS 60!

KNOWN AS LONG SHANKS BECAUSE HE WAS SO TALL

Edward was known as 'Hammer of the Scots' because of his attempts to unite Scotland & England. He took the Scottish crown in 1296 but the Scots retrieved it. Edward died in Cumbria, on his way to invade Scotland again.

The English adopted the Welsh long bow. It was the most accurate & efficient weapon until the invention of gunpowder.

People washed with soap made from goat tallow, beech ash & olive oil.

IN 1295 THE FIRST MODEL PARLIAMENT WAS INTRODUCED. IT HAD TO APPROVE ALL THE LAWS THAT THE KING MADE.

HE WAS ALSO NICKNAMED 'EDWARD THE LAW GIVER' BECAUSE OF HIS MANY LEGAL REFORMS.

CHIRK CASTLE IN CLWYD WAS BUILT TO PROTECT EDWARD'S CONQUESTS IN WALES.

BORN 1239 SUCCEEDED 1272 MARRIED ELEANOR OF CASTILE & MARGARET OF FRANCE DIED 1307 BURIED IN WESTMINSTER ABBEY

ROBIN HOOD

OF WALES

PRINCE

WAS CROWNED

EDWARD II

MANY PEOPLE HAVE TRIED TO PROVE THAT ROBIN HOOD WAS A REAL PERSON. THE CENSUS IN 1230 REFERS TO A FUGITIVE NAMED ROBERT HOOD WHO ESCAPED TO A FOREST IN BARNSDALE YORKSHIRE, NOT SHERWOOD FOREST.

THE STORY OF ROBIN HOOD WAS FIRST PUBLISHED IN ABOUT 1420 AS 'A LYTEL GESTE OF ROBIN HODE: KYNGE EDWARD & ROBIN HODE & LYTEL JOHAN.'

THE CORONATION CHAIR

THE CORONATION STONE IS KEPT UNDER THE CORONATION CHAIR

THE SCOTTISH CORONATION STONE WAS TAKEN TO WESTMINSTER ABBEY BY EDWARD I AFTER HE DEFEATED THE SCOTS.

ENGLAND LOST SCOTLAND FOR THREE CENTURIES AT THE BATTLE OF BANNOCKBURN

EDWARD WAS A WEAK BUT FUN-LOVING KING. HE WAS FORMALLY DEPOSED BY PARLIAMENT AFTER 19 YEARS OF REIGN IN FAVOUR OF HIS SON, EDWARD III.

DURING EDWARD'S REIGN, RICH PEOPLE ATE WHITE BREAD, MEAT, FISH & SWEETMEATS. FOR THE PEASANTS THE CHOICE WAS LIMITED TO DARK BREAD, ALE, CHEESES & POTTAGE.

A PLOUGHMAN EARNED 12 SHILLINGS (60p) A YEAR

BORN AT CAERNARVON CASTLE, EDWARD WAS THE FIRST WELSH PRINCE OF WALES. HE MARRIED ISABELLA (KNOWN AS THE SHE WOLF)

WHEN SHE WAS ONLY 12 YEARS OLD! IN 1327 ISABELLA'S LOVER, MORTIMER, IMPRISONED EDWARD IN BERKELEY CASTLE, GLOUCESTERSHIRE AND FINALLY HAD HIM MURDERED, ALLEGEDLY BY THE INSERTION OF A RED HOT POKER INTO HIS BOWELS.... OUCH!

BORN 1284 SUCCEEDED 1307 MARRIED ISABELLA OF FRANCE DIED 1327 BURIED IN GLOUCESTER CATHEDRAL

EDWARD III RESTORED SCOTIA'S PRIDE

PHILIPPA of HAINAULT

EDWARD & PHILIPPA HAD 12 CHILDREN. SHE WAS A LOVING & CHEERFUL WIFE.

THE BLACK PRINCE

EDWARD'S SON WAS CALLED THE BLACK PRINCE AS HE ALWAYS WORE BLACK ARMOUR. HE DIED BEFORE HIS FATHER AND SO NEVER BECAME KING. HE LOVED WAR MONGERING AND WAS KNOWN TO BE A CRUEL MAN.

MEN'S SHOES WERE SO POINTED THAT THE TOES WERE HELD UP & ATTACHED TO THE KNEES BY SILVER CHAINS.

THE 100 YEARS WAR STARTED BETWEEN ENGLAND & FRANCE.

DAVID II OF SCOTLAND WAS DEFEATED & IMPRISONED WHEN TRYING TO INVADE ENGLAND. EDWARD RELEASED HIM TEN YEARS LATER.

THE BLACK DEATH

IN 1348 THE BLACK DEATH CAME FROM CHINA & KILLED A THIRD OF THE POPULATION IN 2 YEARS. AROUND 2 MILLION BRITONS DIED & 30 MILLION PEOPLE THROUGHOUT EUROPE.

THE DISEASE WAS CARRIED BY RATS

RICHARD II BY HENRY'S HAND DIED

AND SPREAD BY FLEAS

DOCTORS TENDING THE SICK WORE PROTECTIVE CLOTHES & A 'BEAK' OF HERBS TO FILTER THE AIR.

RICHARD WAS THE SON OF THE BLACK PRINCE. HE DIED A PRISONER IN PONTEFRACT CASTLE. HE MAY HAVE BEEN MURDERED ON HENRY BOLINGBROKE'S INSTRUCTION.

BORN 1312 SUCCEEDED 1327 MARRIED PHILIPPA of HAINAULT DIED 1377 BURIED IN WESTMINSTER ABBEY

BORN 1367 SUCCEEDED 1377 MARRIED ANNE of BOHEMIA & ISOBELLA of VALOIS DIED 1400 BURIED AT LANGLEY, LATER WESTMINSTER ABBEY

RICHARD BECAME KING AT THE AGE OF 10. HIS UNCLE, JOHN OF GAUNT, ACTED AS REGENT UNTIL 1385 WHEN RICHARD TOOK CONTROL.

THE PEASANTS' REVOLT

IN 1381 A GOVERNMENT POLL TAX WAS INTRODUCED WHICH LED TO THE PEASANTS' REVOLT. THEIR LEADER, WAT TYLER, MARCHED HIS MEN TO LONDON AND MET THE YOUNG KING WHO PROMISED IMPROVEMENTS BUT WAT TYLER WAS KILLED BY THE LORD MAYOR OF LONDON.

JOHN OF GAUNT

THE CROWN

RICHARD BANISHED HIS COUSIN HENRY BOLINGBROKE AND SEIZED HIS ESTATES. WHEN HENRY RECLAIMED THEM, HE CAPTURED THE KING AND FORCED HIM TO ABDICATE.

HENRY BOLINGBROKE

HENRY IV THEN WORE

HENRY WAS THE SON OF JOHN OF GAUNT

MARY DE BOHUN, HENRY'S FIRST WIFE, DIED GIVING BIRTH TO THEIR 7TH CHILD.

JOAN OF NAVARRE

WOODEN CLOGS WERE WORN TO RAISE FEET OUT OF THE MUD.

HE WAS THE FIRST KING SINCE WILLIAM THE CONQUEROR TO BE BORN IN ENGLAND OF ENGLISH PARENTS. HE REIGNED FOR 13 TURBULENT YEARS, MANAGING TO CRUSH THE REBELLIONS THAT SPRANG UP THROUGHOUT THE LAND.

PILGRIMS WORE BADGES TO IDENTIFY THEMSELVES AS HOLY PEOPLE.

IN 1407 BETHLEHEM HOSPITAL IN LONDON BECAME A LUNATIC ASYLUM AND WAS KNOWN AS BEDLAM.

GEOFFREY CHAUCER, THE GREAT & LEARNED POET, DIED AT THE AGE OF SIXTY. THE LAST 14 YEARS OF HIS LIFE WERE SPENT WRITING THE CANTERBURY TALES.

THE WIFE OF BATH WHO 'HAD FIVE HUSBANDS ALL AT THE CHURCH DOOR' & THE MERCHANT'S STORY ARE BOTH STORIES FROM THE CANTERBURY TALES.

BORN 1367   SUCCEEDED 1399
MARRIED MARY BOHUN & JOAN OF NAVARRE
DIED 1413   BURIED IN CANTERBURY CATHEDRAL

HENRY V PULLED THE FRENCH KING DOWN

HENRY REVIVED EDWARD III'S CLAIM TO THE FRENCH THRONE & SUCCEEDED IN EXTENDING ENGLISH TERRITORY IN FRANCE.

HENRY V WAS KNOWN AS HENRY OF MONMOUTH BEFORE HE BECAME KING.

THE BATTLE OF AGINCOURT IN 1415 RESULTED IN A FAMOUS VICTORY FOR HENRY.

ALTHOUGH OUTNUMBERED BY THE FRENCH, THE ENGLISH USED THE LONGBOW TO DEADLY EFFECT. LONGBOWS WERE MADE OF YEW, ARROWS OF ASH.

DOCTORS BELIEVED THAT SICKNESS WAS DUE TO BAD BLOOD & USED LEECHES TO SUCK IT OUT OF THEIR PATIENTS!

A LEECH

CATHERINE OF FRANCE

BETTER KNOWN AS CATHERINE OF VALOIS, HENRY'S WIFE WAS THE DAUGHTER OF KING CHARLES VI OF FRANCE

HENRY WAS OVER 1.9 METRES TALL. HE WAS A PROFESSIONAL SOLDIER AND A RUTHLESS WARMONGER.

ARMOUR WAS CLEANED BY ROLLING IT IN A BARREL OF SAND.

HENRY DIED IN SEPTEMBER 1422 BEFORE HE COULD SUCCEED TO THE FRENCH THRONE. THE FRENCH KING DIED A MONTH LATER.

THE WHEELBARROW IS BELIEVED TO HAVE BEEN DEVELOPED IN MEDIEVAL TIMES.

BORN 1387 SUCCEEDED 1413
MARRIED CATHERINE OF VALOIS
DIED 1422 BURIED IN WESTMINSTER ABBEY

HENRY VI LOST THE ROSES AND FRANCE

HENRY WAS CROWNED KING OF ENGLAND & FRANCE BUT BY 1453 HE HAD LOST MOST OF FRANCE & ONLY CALAIS REMAINED UNDER HIS RULE. IN 1461 HE ALSO LOST HIS CROWN TO THE YORKISTS.

MARGARET of ANJOU

RICHARD (DICK WHITTINGTON) WAS 3 TIMES LORD MAYOR OF LONDON

DICK WHITTINGTON

THE STORY OF PUSS-IN-BOOTS DEVELOPED AROUND THE HISTORY OF DICK WHITTINGTON.

JOAN of ARC

A DEEPLY RELIGIOUS PEASANT GIRL, JUST 17 YEARS OLD, JOAN LED AN ARMY OF 4000 FRENCH SOLDIERS TO VICTORY AT ORLEANS.

IN 1431 THE ENGLISH CAPTURED HER AND BURNT HER AT THE STAKE IN ROUEN MARKET PLACE FOR WITCHCRAFT.

RED & WHITE BARBERS' POLES SIGNIFIED THE BLOOD AND BANDAGES OF THEIR TRADE. AS WELL AS CUTTING HAIR, THEY WERE ALSO SURGEONS & DENTISTS.

HENRY WAS OFTEN ILL AND AT THESE TIMES HE HANDED OVER CONTROL TO HIS COUSIN, THE DUKE OF YORK. THE DUKE'S SON, EDWARD IV, IMPRISONED HENRY IN THE TOWER OF LONDON WHERE HE WAS MURDERED.

THE WARS of THE ROSES
BITTER RIVALRIES BROKE OUT BETWEEN THE TWO POWERFUL FAMILIES OF YORK & LANCASTER DURING THE REIGN OF LANCASTRIAN HENRY.

LANCASTER

YORK

BORN 1421 SUCCEEDED 1422 AGED 8 MONTHS
MARRIED MARGARET OF ANJOU DIED 1471
BURIED IN CHERTSEY ABBEY, LATER AT WINDSOR

EDWARD IV LED THE COMMONS A DANCE

WILLIAM CAXTON SET UP THE FIRST ENGLISH PRINTING PRESS IN 1476. HE PRINTED ABOUT 80 BOOKS IN HIS LIFETIME INCLUDING 'THE CANTERBURY TALES'.

ELIZABETH WOODVILLE

MIRRORS & COMPASSES WERE INVENTED IN MEDIEVAL TIMES

GUNS & CANNONS CAME INTO USE, AS DID RUDDERS FOR BOATS & SPINNING WHEELS.

THE WOOL & CLOTH TRADE FLOURISHED DURING THIS PERIOD.

EDWARD WAS BRIEFLY DEPOSED FROM THE THRONE BY HIS FORMER FRIEND, THE EARL OF WARWICK IN 1470. EDWARD RETURNED FROM EXILE IN FLANDERS & DEFEATED AND KILLED WARWICK AT THE BATTLE OF BARNET.

EDWARD V WAS SLAIN WITH HIS BROTHER

EDWARD V WAS ARRESTED BY HIS UNCLE, THE EARL OF GLOUCESTER, AFTER JUST 11 WEEKS' REIGN. HE WAS IMPRISONED IN THE TOWER WITH HIS YOUNGER BROTHER. AFTER RICHARD WAS CROWNED BOTH BOYS WERE MURDERED.

TOWER OF LONDON

EDWARD IV WAS OUTSTANDINGLY HANDSOME BUT HIS LIFESTYLE CAUSED HIM TO BECOME GROSSLY FAT AND DISEASED.

BORN 1442 SUCCEEDED 1461
MARRIED ELIZABETH WOODVILLE
DIED 1483 BURIED AT WINDSOR

BORN 1470 SUCCEEDED 1483
DIED 1483 BURIED IN THE TOWER
200 YEARS LATER IN WESTMINSTER ABBEY

ANNE & RICHARD HAD ONE SON WHO DIED IN INFANCY.

ANNE NEVILLE

THE MAJORITY OF PEOPLE DIED BEFORE THEY WERE 50. DOCTORS TRIED SPELLS & CHARMS TO CURE THE SICK & OINTMENTS MADE FROM DUNG, BLOOD & ANIMAL FAT.

GUILDS

TRADES WERE REPRESENTED BY GUILDS. BOYS WERE 'APPRENTICED' TO LEARN A TRADE AND AFTER SEVEN YEARS BECAME 'JOURNEYMEN' IF THEIR WORK WAS OF THE REQUIRED STANDARD. YEARS LATER THEY WOULD MAKE A 'MASTERPIECE' TO TEST THEIR SKILLS. IF IT WAS GOOD ENOUGH, THEY WOULD BE TAKEN INTO THE GUILD & BECOME MASTER CRAFTSMEN.

IT WAS THE FASHION FOR NOBLE WOMEN TO WEAR VERY LARGE GRAND HATS.

THE DUKE OF YORK, EDWARD'S YOUNGER BROTHER

RICHARD WAS RUMOURED TO HAVE BEEN RESPONSIBLE FOR THE MURDER OF THE PRINCES. HOWEVER SOME HISTORIANS NOW THINK THE BOYS WERE KILLED ON THE ORDERS OF HENRY VII, THE TUDOR KING WHO SEIZED THE CROWN FROM RICHARD III.

THE WINDMILL, USED TO GRIND CORN INTO FLOUR, WAS A MEDIEVAL INVENTION.

RICHARD WAS KNOWN AS 'CROOKBACK' OR 'CROUCHBACK' BECAUSE HIS RIGHT SHOULDER WAS HUNCHED AND HIS LEFT HAND SHRIVELLED.

RICHARD III WAS THE LAST OF THE PLANTAGENETS

BORN 1452 SUCCEEDED 1483 MARRIED ANNE NEVILLE DIED 1485 BURIED AT GREY FRIARS ABBEY

HENRY VII WAS FRUGAL of MEANS

HENRY VIII

HENRY VII WAS THE FIRST TUDOR KING. THE TUDORS, OR TWDWRS, REIGNED FOR 120 YEARS.

ELIZABETH of YORK

HENRY WAS A LANCASTRIAN AND MARRIED A YORKIST TO UNITE THE WARRING FAMILIES.

1st WIFE

CATHERINE of ARAGON

WIDOW OF HENRY'S BROTHER, ARTHUR, & MOTHER OF MARY. HENRY DIVORCED HER IN 1533.

SIR THOMAS MORE

THOMAS CROMWELL

THESE TWO POWERFUL MEN PAID A HEAVY PRICE FOR THEIR AMBITIONS. HAVING LOST FAVOUR WITH HENRY, BOTH WERE EXECUTED

CHRISTOPHER COLUMBUS

LEONARDO DA VINCI

BY AVOIDING COSTLY WARS, PROMOTING TRADE & IMPOSING NEW TAXES, HENRY IMPROVED ROYAL REVENUES & DIED A RICH MAN.

THE ARABIC MATHEMATICAL SYMBOLS + x AND = CAME INTO USE AT THE END OF THE 15TH CENTURY.

COLUMBUS DISCOVERED THE AMERICAS FOR THE SPANISH KING IN 1492, AND BROUGHT BACK COCOA, PINEAPPLES AND TURKEYS TO EUROPE FROM THE WEST INDIES.

FAMOUS FOR PAINTING THE MONA LISA IN 1503, LEONARDO WAS ALSO AN ENGINEER, INVENTOR, WRITER & ARCHITECT.

BORN 1457 SUCCEEDED 1485 MARRIED ELIZABETH of YORK DIED 1509 BURIED IN WESTMINSTER ABBEY

HAD TOO MANY QUEENS

ANNE 2ND BOLEYN WIFE

JANE SEYMOUR 3RD WIFE

MOTHER OF EDWARD, THE SON THAT HENRY SO DESPERATELY DESIRED, JANE DIED 12 DAYS AFTER GIVING BIRTH.

ANNE OF CLEEVES 4TH WIFE

THE CROWDS JEERED AT ANNE'S CORONATION. SHE HAD A DAUGHTER, ELIZABETH, BUT COULD NOT GIVE HENRY A SON. SHE WAS ACCUSED OF ADULTERY AND BEHEADED.

HAVING SEEN A FLATTERING PORTRAIT OF ANNE, HENRY WAS PERSUADED TO MARRY HER. BUT WHEN HE MET HER HE CALLED HER 'THE FLANDERS MARE'. THE MARRIAGE WAS ANNULLED AFTER SIX MONTHS.

5TH WIFE

CATHERINE HOWARD

HENRY WAS 50 WHEN HE MARRIED CATHERINE. AT FIRST HE WAS DELIGHTED WITH HIS YOUNG WIFE, BUT HE SOON BECAME CONSUMED WITH JEALOUSY. SHE WAS EXECUTED FOR ADULTERY AND SO WERE HER LOVERS.

HANDSOME & ATHLETIC WHEN YOUNG, HENRY BECAME VERY FAT LATER IN LIFE. HIS BED WAS 4 METRES WIDE & HE NEEDED ROPES & PULLIES TO HELP HIM GET IN & OUT OF IT! HE SUFFERED FROM BLEEDING GUMS & LEG ULCERS & WAS BAD-TEMPERED & DEPRESSED IN HIS LATER YEARS.

6TH WIFE

CATHERINE PARR

THE ONLY ONE OF HIS WIVES TO SURVIVE HIM, SHE NURSED HIM IN HIS FINAL YEARS.

HENRY WAS OBSESSED WITH THE NEED FOR A MALE HEIR.

HE WAS KNOWN AS 'BLUFF KING HAL'.

EXPENSIVE WARS WITH SCOTLAND & FRANCE HAD ALMOST BANKRUPTED THE TREASURY.

HENRY ARGUED WITH THE POPE WHEN HE WOULD NOT ALLOW THE KING TO DIVORCE HIS FIRST WIFE, SO HENRY MADE HIMSELF HEAD OF THE CHURCH OF ENGLAND. CONVENTS & MONASTERIES WERE DESTROYED AND THEIR LAND AND TREASURES SOLD.

BORN 1491 SUCCEEDED 1509
MARRIED SIX WIVES
DIED 1547 BURIED AT WINDSOR

EDWARD VI REFORMATION BEGAN

LADY JANE GREY

REIGNED FOR 9 DAYS. THE THRONE WAS THEN CLAIMED BY THE CATHOLIC MARY AND LADY JANE WAS EXECUTED ALONG WITH HER HUSBAND, DUDLEY, AND THE DUKE OF NORTHUMBERLAND.

DURING EDWARD'S REIGN, TWO PROTECTORS HELPED THE BOY KING TO GOVERN. THE FIRST WAS EDWARD SEYMOUR, THE DUKE OF SOMERSET (EDWARD'S UNCLE). THE DUKE OF NORTHUMBERLAND BECAME THE SECOND (PROTECTOR) IN 1550. HE PERSUADED EDWARD TO DISINHERIT THE PRINCESSES, MARY & ELIZABETH IN FAVOUR OF EDWARD'S COUSIN, LADY JANE GREY.

EDWARD SEYMOUR

EDWARD VI SUCCEEDED AT THE AGE OF NINE. HE WAS A KEEN PROTESTANT & HE INTRODUCED A NEW PRAYER BOOK. DURING EDWARD'S REIGN THE RELIGIOUS REFORMATION WAS AT ITS HEIGHT. CATHOLICS WERE NOT ALLOWED TO PRACTICE THEIR RELIGION AND MANY STATUES AND PAINTINGS IN THEIR CHURCHES WERE DESTROYED.

GOOSE FEATHERS WERE USED FOR WRITING. LATIN WAS THE MOST IMPORTANT SUBJECT.

HAIR WAS WASHED JUST 3 OR 4 TIMES A YEAR WITH WATER & WOOD-ASH.

HONEY WAS USED AS A SWEETENER.

EDWARD WAS BETROTHED TO MARY QUEEN OF SCOTS, BUT THEY NEVER MARRIED.

KING PHILIP II OF SPAIN

PHILIP AND MARY LIVED TOGETHER FOR JUST ONE YEAR OF THEIR MARRIAGE. THEY HAD NO CHILDREN AND THEIR UNION WAS NOT A HAPPY ONE.

PUNISHMENT WAS HARSH. THIEVES WERE BRANDED (MARKS BURNT ON THEIR SKIN) AND THE RACK STRETCHED THE TRUTH OUT OF PEOPLE.

PUPILS WERE BEATEN WITH BIRCHES FOR PUNISHMENT.

BORN 1537 SUCCEEDED 1547
DIED 1553
BURIED IN WESTMINSTER ABBEY

BLOODY MARY FRUSTRATED THE PLAN

THOMAS CRANMER

'BLOODY' QUEEN MARY IMMEDIATELY REINSTATED CATHOLICISM.

SHE EARNED HER NICKNAME BY BURNING PROTESTANTS AS HERETICS.

MARY WAS DRAWN INTO WAR WITH THE FRENCH AND LOST CALAIS, THE LAST ENGLISH POSSESSION IN FRANCE.

ONCE ARCHBISHOP OF CANTERBURY, HE WAS BURNT AT THE STAKE IN 1556 AT OXFORD. HE HAD MADE AN ENEMY OF MARY DURING HENRY VIII'S REIGN BY DECLARING HER TO BE ILLEGITIMATE & HER MOTHER'S MARRIAGE TO HENRY NULL & VOID.

WOMEN SUSPECTED OF WITCHCRAFT WERE SUBJECTED TO THE DUCKING STOOL. IF THEY SURVIVED A 'DUCKING' THEY WERE GUILTY, BUT IF THEY DROWNED THEY WERE INNOCENT!

COMMON PEOPLE WERE HANGED FOR THEIR WRONGDOINGS

BUT NOBLEMEN WERE BEHEADED

BORN 1516 SUCCEEDED 1553 MARRIED PHILIP of SPAIN DIED 1558 BURIED IN WESTMINSTER ABBEY

WISE AND PROFOUND WERE ELIZABETH'S WAYS

'GLORIANA', OR 'GOOD QUEEN BESS', AS SHE WAS KNOWN, HAD OVER 1000 GOWNS IN HER WARDROBE. SHE PAINTED HER FACE WITH WHITE LEAD & VINEGAR & USED RED DYE AND EGG WHITE FOR HER CHEEKS.

HER HAIR WAS NATURALLY RED. IN LATER LIFE SHE WENT BALD AND WORE A BRIGHT RED WIG. SHE WAS KNOWN TO 'SWEAR LIKE A TROOPER'!

THE 'RAINBOW PORTRAIT' BY ISAAC OLIVER DEPICTED ELIZABETH WEARING A CLOAK WITH A PATTERN OF EARS & EYES, SUGGESTING SHE 'HEARS & SEES ALL'. ON THE SLEEVE A SERPENT SYMBOLISES PRUDENCE.

HER TEETH WERE BLACK, DUE TO EATING TOO MANY SWEETS OR 'COMFITS'. SHE WAS FAMOUS FOR THE CLEANLINESS OF HER LINEN & THE SWEET SMELL OF HER PERFUME.

WILLIAM SHAKESPEARE OFTEN CALLED THE WORLD'S GREATEST PLAYWRIGHT

THE POPULATION OF ENGLAND ALMOST DOUBLED BETWEEN HENRY VIII'S REIGN AND THE ELIZABETHAN AGE, FROM AROUND 2 MILLION TO JUST OVER 4 MILLION.

SIR FRANCIS DRAKE KNOWN AS 'EL DRAKO' BY THE SPANISH, HE ATTACKED SPANISH PORTS IN AMERICA & WAS THE FIRST ENGLISHMAN TO SAIL AROUND THE WORLD. DRAKE'S SHIP WAS CALLED THE GOLDEN HIND.

ANGERED BY THE CONSTANT ATTACKS ON HIS SHIPS, PHILIP OF SPAIN SENT AN ARMADA OF SHIPS TO INVADE ENGLAND IN 1588. HE WANTED TO SEIZE THE ENGLISH CROWN AND RETURN THE PEOPLE TO THE CATHOLIC FAITH, BUT DRAKE SET FIRE TO THE SPANISH FLEET WITH FIRE SHIPS. MOST OF THE SHIPS THAT ESCAPED WERE DESTROYED BY FIERCE STORMS.

ROBERT DUDLEY

THE EARL OF LEICESTER WAS BELIEVED TO HAVE BEEN THE QUEEN'S ONLY LOVE ♥

BORN 1533 SUCCEEDED 1558
DIED 1603
BURIED IN WESTMINSTER ABBEY

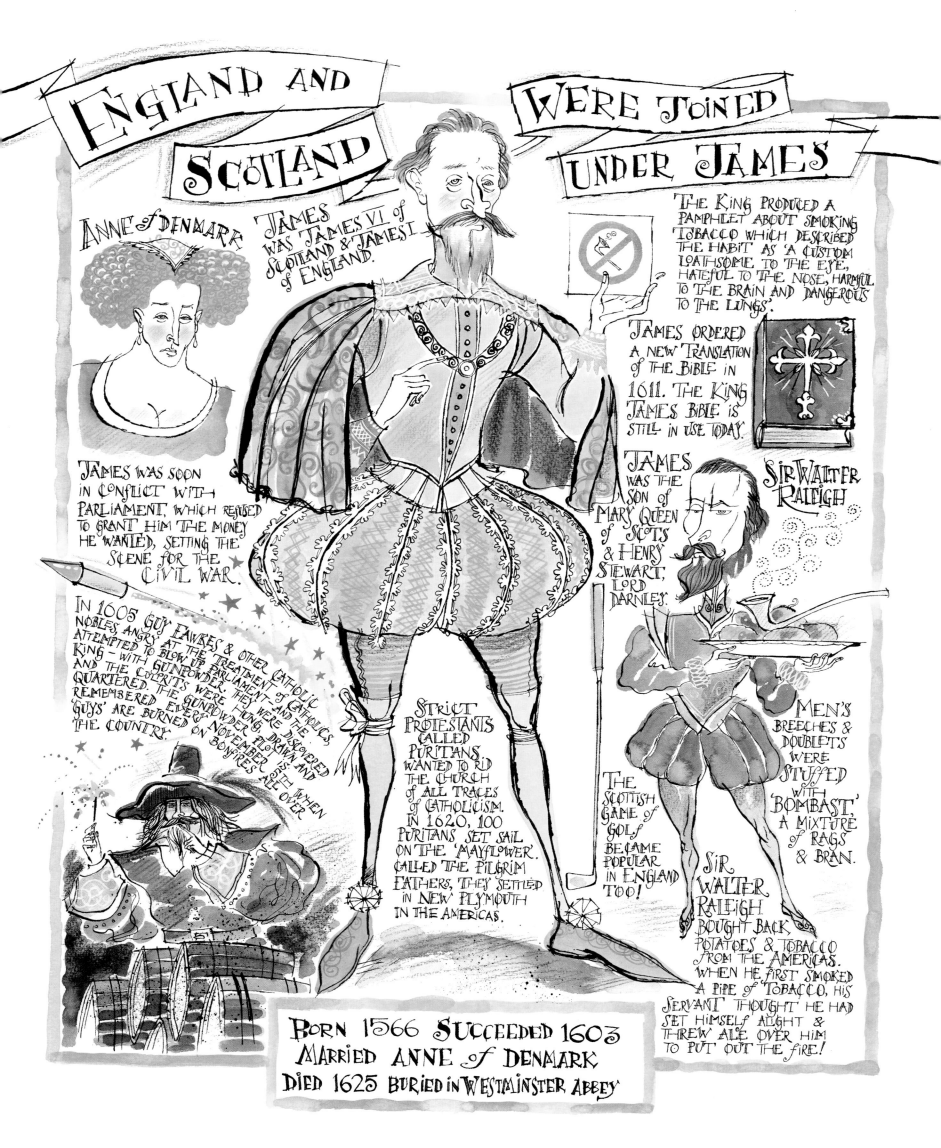

ENGLAND AND SCOTLAND WERE JOINED UNDER JAMES

ANNE of DENMARK

JAMES WAS JAMES VI of SCOTLAND & JAMES I of ENGLAND.

THE KING PRODUCED A PAMPHLET ABOUT SMOKING TOBACCO WHICH DESCRIBED THE HABIT AS 'A CUSTOM LOATHSOME TO THE EYE, HATEFUL TO THE NOSE, HARMFUL TO THE BRAIN AND DANGEROUS TO THE LUNGS'.

JAMES ORDERED A NEW TRANSLATION OF THE BIBLE IN 1611. THE KING JAMES BIBLE IS STILL IN USE TODAY.

JAMES WAS THE SON of MARY QUEEN of SCOTS & HENRY STEWART, LORD DARNLEY.

SIR WALTER RALEIGH

JAMES WAS SOON IN CONFLICT WITH PARLIAMENT, WHICH REFUSED TO GRANT HIM THE MONEY HE WANTED, SETTING THE SCENE FOR THE CIVIL WAR.

IN 1605 GUY FAWKES & OTHER CATHOLIC NOBLES, ANGRY AT THE TREATMENT of CATHOLICS, ATTEMPTED TO BLOW UP PARLIAMENT - AND THE KING - WITH GUNPOWDER. THEY WERE DISCOVERED AND THE CULPRITS WERE HUNG, DRAWN AND QUARTERED. THE GUNPOWDER PLOT IS REMEMBERED EVERY NOVEMBER 5TH WHEN 'GUYS' ARE BURNED ON BONFIRES ALL OVER THE COUNTRY.

STRICT PROTESTANTS CALLED PURITANS WANTED TO RID THE CHURCH of ALL TRACES of CATHOLICISM. IN 1620, 100 PURITANS SET SAIL ON THE 'MAYFLOWER'. CALLED THE PILGRIM FATHERS, THEY SETTLED IN NEW PLYMOUTH IN THE AMERICAS.

THE SCOTTISH GAME of GOLF BECAME POPULAR IN ENGLAND TOO!

MEN'S BREECHES & DOUBLETS WERE STUFFED WITH 'BOMBAST', A MIXTURE of RAGS & BRAN.

SIR WALTER RALEIGH BOUGHT BACK POTATOES & TOBACCO FROM THE AMERICAS. WHEN HE FIRST SMOKED A PIPE of TOBACCO, HIS SERVANT THOUGHT HE HAD SET HIMSELF ALIGHT & THREW ALE OVER HIM TO PUT OUT THE FIRE!

BORN 1566 SUCCEEDED 1603
MARRIED ANNE of DENMARK
DIED 1625 BURIED IN WESTMINSTER ABBEY

CHARLES FOUND THE PEOPLE

A CRUEL CORRECTOR

ROYALISTS

SUPPORTERS OF THE KING LOVED COLOURFUL EXPENSIVE CLOTHES ADORNED WITH LACE & RIBBONS.

CHARLES WALKED WITH A LIMP AND STUTTERED, BUT HE TOOK GREAT PRIDE IN HIS APPEARANCE.

HENRIETTA MARIA DAUGHTER of HENRY IV of FRANCE

CHARLES, LIKE HIS FATHER JAMES I BELIEVED IN THE DEVINE RIGHT of KINGS (THE BELIEF THAT A KING WAS GIVEN THE RIGHT TO RULE BY GOD SO TO REBEL AGAINST HIM WAS A SIN). HE DISSOLVED PARLIAMENT WHEN HE DISAGREED WITH IT, ONCE FOR 11 YEARS WHEN HE RULED AS A DICTATOR. THE RIFT BETWEEN THE KING & PARLIAMENT FINALLY LED TO THE OUTBREAK OF THE CIVIL WAR IN 1642.

ON THE COLD JANUARY DAY of HIS EXECUTION, CHARLES WORE AN EXTRA SHIRT TO ENSURE THAT HE DIDN'T SHIVER & APPEAR TO BE AFRAID.

CHARLES LIKED SURPRISE PIES ONE ACUALLY CONTAINED FOUR-AND-TWENTY BLACK BIRDS!

FRANCIS BACON, PHILOSOPHER & SCIENTIST, DIED of A COLD IN 1626, CAUGHT WHILST STUFFING A CHICKEN WITH ICE IN AN EXPERIMENT TO PRESERVE MEAT.

MEN WONDERED THAT SO GOOD A MAN SHOULD BE SO BAD A KING.

CHARLES' MARRIAGE WAS TEMPESTUOUS IN THE BEGINNING. ONCE AN AMBASSADOR WAS CALLED TO SETTLE A DISPUTE BETWEEN THE KING & HIS WIFE OVER THE WEATHER! BUT THEIR RELATIONSHIP IMPROVED AND HENRIETTA SUPPORTED HIM THROUGH HIS TROUBLES.

A CAVALIER

BORN 1600 SUCCEEDED 1625 MARRIED HENRIETTA MARIA DIED 1649 BURIED IN WESTMINSTER ABBEY

OLIVER CROMWELL

BECAME LORD PROTECTOR

ROUNDHEADS WORE ARMOUR & FOUGHT WITH MUSKETS, SWORDS & PISTOLS. THEY WERE WELL ORGANISED. DURING BATTLE THEY SURROUNDED THEMSELVES WITH A PROTECTIVE 'HEDGE' OF 6-METRE LONG PIKES.

CROMWELL'S BODY WAS DUG UP & HUNG ON THE GALLOWS IN CHARLES II'S REIGN.

OLIVER CROMWELL WAS CHAIRMAN OF THE COUNCIL OF STATE FROM 1649 WHEN A REPUBLIC KNOWN AS THE COMMONWEALTH WAS SET UP. IN 1653 HE DISMISSED THE 'RUMP' PARLIAMENT & RULED AS LORD PROTECTOR. ONE OF ENGLAND'S GREATEST MILITARY COMMANDERS, CROMWELL TRAINED THE 'NEW MODEL ARMY' WHICH DEFEATED THE ROYALISTS AT THE BATTLE OF NASEBY IN 1645.

WHEN CROMWELL DIED, HIS SON RICHARD SUCCEEDED HIM AS PROTECTOR BUT WAS AN INEFFECTIVE RULER & WAS DEPOSED IN 1659.

PURITANS BELIEVED IN PLAIN CLOTHES, SIMPLE LIVING AND HARD WORK. CROMWELL LIVED BY THESE STRICT PRINCIPLES.

LAWS WERE PASSED AGAINST SWEARING, DANCING, CARD PLAYING AND FOOTBALL. THEATRES & INNS WERE CLOSED & EVEN CHRISTMAS DINNER WAS FORBIDDEN.

PIKES USED BY INFANTRY-MEN

CROMWELL'S TROOPS WERE CALLED ROUNDHEADS BECAUSE THEY WORE METAL HELMETS & HAD THEIR HAIR CUT SHORT.

A ROUNDHEAD

BORN 1599 BECAME CHAIRMAN OF THE COUNCIL OF STATE 1649 BECAME LORD PROTECTOR 1653 DIED 1658 BURIED IN WESTMINSTER ABBEY

CHARLES II HID IN AN OAK

CATHERINE OF BRAGANZA

NELL GWYN
FAVOURITE OF THE KING'S MISTRESSES

CHARLES AND CATHERINE HAD NO CHILDREN BUT CHARLES HAD MANY ILLEGITIMATE OFFSPRING. ONE SON, THE DUKE OF MONMOUTH, TRIED TO SEIZE THE CROWN ON HIS DEATH. HE WAS DEFEATED BY JAMES II AT THE BATTLE OF SEDGEMOOR.

AROUND 1680 THE DODO, A FLIGHTLESS BIRD, BECAME EXTINCT.

KNOWN AS 'THE MERRY MONARCH', CHARLES LOVED TO DANCE & ENJOY HIMSELF. HIS STYLE WAS POPULAR WITH THE PEOPLE AFTER THE DULL DAYS OF THE PAST.

CHARLES WAS ON THE RUN FROM CROMWELL'S ARMY FOR SIX WEEKS DURING THE CIVIL WAR. MANY INNS ARE CALLED 'THE ROYAL OAK' AFTER HIS NARROW ESCAPE FROM CAPTURE BY HIDING IN AN OAK TREE.

THE GREAT FIRE OF LONDON STARTED IN A BAKER'S SHOP IN PUDDING LANE IN 1666. IT RAGED FOR 4 DAYS & DESTROYED MUCH OF THE CITY. SIR CHRISTOPHER WREN WAS ASKED TO DESIGN A NEW CITY. HIS MASTERPIECE WAS ST. PAUL'S CATHEDRAL.

SIR CHRISTOPHER WREN

BUILT OR RESTORED OVER FIFTY LONDON CHURCHES.

IN 1665 THE BUBONIC PLAGUE BROKE OUT KILLING 68,000 PEOPLE IN LONDON ALONE. CARTERS WALKED THE STREETS CALLING, 'BRING OUT YOUR DEAD'. THE BODIES WERE TAKEN TO PITS AND COVERED WITH QUICK LIME. RED CROSSES WERE PAINTED ON THE DOORS OF INFECTED HOUSES.

THE MONARCHY WAS RESTORED, BUT PARLIAMENTS' POWERS INCREASED. TWO POLITICAL PARTIES STARTED TO EMERGE, THE 'COUNTRY' PARTY, WHICH BECAME THE WHIGS AND THE 'COURT' PARTY (THE KING'S SUPPORTERS) WHICH BECAME THE TORIES.

BORN 1630 SUCCEEDED 1660 MARRIED CATHERINE OF BRAGANZA DIED 1685 BURIED IN WESTMINSTER ABBEY

JAMES II

SIR ISAAC NEWTON

IN 1665 HE DISCOVERED THE LAW OF GRAVITY WHEN HE WATCHED AN APPLE FALL FROM A TREE. KING CHARLES WAS INTERESTED IN SCIENCE AND FOUNDED THE ROYAL SOCIETY FOR SCIENTISTS, ASTRONOMERS & DOCTORS.

PUPPIES' URINE WAS RECOMMENDED FOR THE COMPLEXION.

SAMUEL PEPYS

WROTE A PERSONAL DIARY WHICH IS A USEFUL ACCOUNT OF LIFE IN LONDON AT THE TIME OF CHARLES II.

JAMES ANGERED THE COMMONS BY PROMOTING CATHOLIC CAUSES IN PARLIAMENT. HE WAS TOLERATED ONLY BECAUSE HIS DAUGHTERS, WHO WERE LIKELY TO SUCCEED HIM, WERE PROTESTANTS. BUT WHEN HIS SECOND WIFE, A CATHOLIC, BORE HIM A SON, THE POWERFUL PROTESTANT GOVERNMENT SENT FOR MARY, JAMES'S PROTESTANT DAUGHTER AND HER HUSBAND, WILLIAM of ORANGE. THEIR PEACEFUL INVASION IS KNOWN AS 'THE GLORIOUS REVOLUTION'.

MARY of MODENA

ENGLAND'S ONLY ITALIAN QUEEN

JUDGE JEFFREYS

THE DUKE of MONMOUTH LED A REBELLION AGAINST THE KING, BUT HE WAS DEFEATED AND EXECUTED. THE HANGING JUDGE' DEALT WITH THE REST. JEFFREYS, KNOWN AS THE 'HANGING JUDGE' DEALT MORE THAN 300 WERE HANGED AND MANY MORE WERE TRANSPORTED TO AMERICA AS SLAVES.

WHEN WILLIAM & MARY INVADED ENGLAND, JAMES FLED TO FRANCE. AS HE CROSSED THE THAMES HE THREW THE SEALS of GOVERNMENT OVERBOARD!

BORN 1633 SUCCEEDED 1685
MARRIED ANNE HYDE & MARY of MODENA (ABDICATED 1688)
DIED 1701 BURIED AT ST.GERMAIN, FRANCE

WILLIAM & MARY

NEXT SHARED THE THRONE

WHEN SEEKING MARY'S HAND IN MARRIAGE, WILLIAM DRANK HER UNCLE, CHARLES II, UNDER THE TABLE!

PARLIAMENT ISSUED A DECLARATION (OR BILL) OF RIGHTS, MAKING WILLIAM & MARY 'JOINT' SOVEREIGNS & EXCLUDING CATHOLICS FROM THE SUCCESSION.

THE BANK OF ENGLAND WAS ESTABLISHED IN 1694. THE GOVERNMENT BORROWED FROM IT THUS CREATING THE 'NATIONAL DEBT'.

PUBLIC BATHS WERE OPENED FOR THOSE WHO COULD AFFORD THEM.

WILLIAM FELL FROM HIS HORSE WHEN IT STUMBLED ON A MOLE HILL. PNEUMONIA SET IN AND HE DIED A FEW DAYS LATER. WHEN HIS JACOBITE ENEMIES (SUPPORTERS OF JAMES II) HEARD THE NEWS THEY DRANK A TOAST TO THE 'LITTLE GENTLEMAN IN VELVET' (THE MOLE)!

WILLIAM & MARY BOUGHT DUTCH FURNITURE, CHINA & PAINTINGS WITH THEM TO ENGLAND. DUTCH STYLE BECAME VERY FASHIONABLE.

COAL WAS MINED IN NEWCASTLE AND TRANSPORTED TO LONDON BY SEA.

SMALL BOYS WERE USED AS CHIMNEY SWEEPS IN LARGE HOUSES. THEY HAD TO CLIMB UP INSIDE THE CHIMNEY.

HIGHWAYMEN HELD UP CARRIAGES, ROBBING WEALTHY TRAVELLERS ON REMOTE ROADS.

POST BOYS ON HORSEBACK CARRIED THE MAIL. A LETTER WOULD TAKE ABOUT 10 DAYS FROM LONDON TO SCOTLAND.

WILLIAM III		MARY II
BORN 1650	SUCCEEDED 1689	BORN 1662
DIED 1702		DIED 1694

BOTH BURIED IN WESTMINSTER ABBEY

EDMUND HALLEY

IN 1705 HALLEY PREDICTED THE RETURN OF "HIS" COMET IN 1758.

ANNE HAD EIGHTEEN PREGNANCIES, BUT ONLY five CHILDREN WERE BORN ALIVE. SADLY, ALL five DIED YOUNG, SO THERE WAS NO DIRECT HEIR. ANNE'S COUSIN, SOPHIA of HANOVER, WAS DECLARED HEIR TO THE THRONE BUT SHE DIED IN 1714 (2 MONTHS BEFORE ANNE) AND SO SOPHIA'S SON, GEORGE, BECAME NEXT IN LINE.

CHARLES II REMARKED of ANNE'S HUSBAND, "I HAVE TRIED HIM DRUNK & I HAVE TRIED HIM SOBER & EITHER WAY THERE IS NOTHING IN HIM." HE CONSIDERED GEORGE TO BE A "NINCOMPOOP"!

CRICKET BECAME A POPULAR SPORT, ALONG WITH BOWLING, COCK-FIGHTING & BEAR-BAITING.

THE PIANO WAS INVENTED IN 1709 BY THE ITALIAN, BARTOLOMEO CRISTOFORI.

PRINCE GEORGE of DENMARK

BORN 1665 SUCCEEDED 1702 MARRIED PRINCE GEORGE of DENMARK DIED 1714 BURIED IN WESTMINSTER ABBEY

GEORGE I FROM HANOVER, CAME

SOPHIA DOROTHEA

GEORGE SPOKE LITTLE ENGLISH. HE CAME TO ENGLAND FOR THE FIRST TIME AS THE NEW KING. HE WAS 54 YEARS OLD.

GEORGE IMPRISONED HIS WIFE FOR 32 YEARS, UNTIL HER DEATH, TO PUNISH HER FOR HAVING AN AFFAIR WITH A SWEDISH COUNT. THE COUNT MYSTERIOUSLY DISAPPEARED. HIS BONES WERE FOUND UNDER HER DRESSING ROOM FLOORBOARDS TWENTY YEARS LATER.

'LADY MONTAGU CALLED HIM "AN HONEST BLOCKHEAD, MORE PROPERLY DULL THAN LAZY."

PRESS GANGS FORCED MEN TO BECOME SAILORS - IF THEY DID NOT OBEY ORDERS THEY WERE FLOGGED WITH A CAT-O-NINE TAILS.

DANIEL DEFOE WROTE 'ROBINSON CRUSOE' IN 1719 AND JONATHAN SWIFT'S 'GULLIVER'S TRAVELS' WAS PUBLISHED IN 1726.

SIR ROBERT WALPOLE

SIR ROBERT WALPOLE BECAME THE FIRST PRIME MINISTER IN 1721 (ALTHOUGH THE TITLE DID NOT BECOME OFFICIAL UNTIL 1905). WALPOLE WAS LITERALLY THE FIRST OR PRIMARY MINISTER, REPRESENTING THE KING IN PARLIAMENT BECAUSE GEORGE COULD NOT UNDERSTAND A WORD.

GEORGE DIED IN OSNABRÜCK IN GERMANY AFTER SUFFERING A STROKE CAUSED BY EATING UNRIPE FRUIT WHEN UNWELL FROM SEA-SICKNESS.

THE SURNAME OF THE ROYAL FAMILY WAS GUELPH

BORN 1660 SUCCEEDED 1714 MARRIED SOPHIA DOROTHEA DIED 1727 BURIED IN HANOVER.

GEORGE II CARRIED ON THE NAME

CAROLINE of ANSBACH

THE KING WALKED WITH A MILITARY STRUT BUT A POPULAR RHYME OF THE DAY WAS, 'YOU MAY STRUT, DAPPER GEORGE, BUT T'WILL ALL BE IN VAIN. WE KNOW 'TIS QUEEN CAROLINE, NOT YOU, THAT REIGN.'

THE PUBLIC COULD PAY TO WATCH THE ROYAL FAMILY EATING.

BOAR GREASE WAS USED AS A HAIR RESTORER.

FASHIONABLE LADIES WORE POWDERED WIGS DECORATED WITH IMITATION FRUIT AND FLOWERS AND SOMETIMES A HUGE HAT ON TOP.

HENRY FIELDING

IN 1750 STARTED THE FIRST DETECTIVE FORCE, LATER KNOWN AS THE BOW STREET RUNNERS.

GEORGE SPOKE ENGLISH WITH A STRONG GERMAN ACCENT. A MAN OF MILITARY PRECISION, WHEN GEORGE VISITED A FRIEND HE WOULD WAIT OUTSIDE THE DOOR AT THE APPOINTED HOUR, WATCH IN HAND, IN ORDER TO ARRIVE AT EXACTLY THE RIGHT TIME. GEORGE WAS THE LAST MONARCH TO LEAD HIS TROOPS INTO BATTLE, DEFEATING THE FRENCH AT DETTINGEN IN 1743.

Tick Tick

IN 1752 BRITAIN ADOPTED THE 'NEW STYLE' GREGORIAN CALENDAR TO CORRECT THE OLD JULIAN CALENDAR. AN EXTRA 11 DAYS WERE ADDED & THE START OF THE YEAR WAS MOVED BACK FROM 25TH MARCH TO 1ST JANUARY.

THE FOURTH EARL of SANDWICH

A COMPULSIVE GAMBLER, HE DEMANDED THAT MEAT BE ENVELOPED IN BREAD AND BROUGHT TO HIM AT THE CARD TABLES SO THAT HE COULD CONTINUE TO PLAY EVEN WHEN HUNGRY. THUS HE INVENTED THE SANDWICH!

BONNIE PRINCE CHARLIE

THE JACOBITE REBELS (SUPPORTERS OF JAMES II) FINALLY FAILED IN THEIR ATTEMPTS TO PUT JAMES'S GRANDSON, CHARLES, ON THE THRONE AT THE BATTLE of CULLODEN IN 1746.

10 DOWNING STREET WAS MADE THE OFFICIAL HOME OF THE PRIME MINISTER IN THE 1730'S.

BORN 1683 SUCCEEDED 1727 MARRIED CAROLINE of BRANDENBURG-ANSBACH DIED 1760 BURIED IN WESTMINSTER ABBEY

GEORGE III WAS LOVED IN THE LAND

QUEEN CHARLOTTE

GEORGE II's SON, FREDERICK, DIED BEFORE HIS FATHER SO THE CROWN SKIPPED A GENERATION, PASSING TO FREDERICK'S SON, GEORGE.

ADMIRAL NELSON

BORN AND EDUCATED IN ENGLAND, GEORGE III WAS THE FIRST KING FOR OVER 50 YEARS TO SPEAK ENGLISH WITHOUT A GERMAN ACCENT.

NELSON DEFEATED THE FRENCH BUT WAS MORTALLY WOUNDED AT THE BATTLE OF TRAFALGAR IN 1805.

CAPTAIN COOK IN 1770 HE EXPLORED NEW ZEALAND AND CLAIMED EAST AUSTRALIA FOR BRITAIN. THE FIRST CONVICTS WERE SENT TO NEW SOUTH WALES IN 1788.

THE FRENCH EMPEROR, NAPOLEON, STRUCK AGAIN IN 1815 BUT WAS DEFEATED AT THE BATTLE OF WATERLOO BY WELLINGTON.

GEORGE III SUFFERED FROM ATTACKS OF A RARE ILLNESS CALLED PORPHYRIA, WHICH MADE HIM FOAM AT THE MOUTH AND APPEAR INSANE.

WOMEN OF FASHION ARRANGED THEIR HAIR OVER WIRE FRAMES UP TO 2 METRES HIGH, PLASTERED IT WITH POMATUM (APPLE AND HOG'S GREASE) AND SPRINKLED FLOUR ON TOP! THE FRAMES HAD TRAP DOORS TO REMOVE VERMIN AND ALLOW THE SCALP TO BE SCRATCHED!

GEORGE WASHINGTON 1ST PRESIDENT of THE UNITED STATES of AMERICA ON 4TH of JULY 1776 THE 13 COLONIES of AMERICA DECLARED THEIR INDEPENDENCE FROM BRITAIN.

THE 'TIMES' APPEARED FOR THE FIRST TIME IN 1788.

SIR HUMPHRY DAVY INVENTED THE MINERS' SAFETY LAMP.

HAIR WAS WASHED ABOUT TWICE A YEAR

THIS WAS A GREAT PERIOD of CHANGE. INVENTIONS INCLUDED JAMES HARGREAVES' SPINNING JENNY AND JAMES WATT'S ROTARY STEAM ENGINE.

BORN 1738 SUCCEEDED 1760 MARRIED CHARLOTTE SOPHIA DIED 1820 BURIED AT WINDSOR

GEORGE IV WAS POMPOUS & GRAND

WHILE HE WAS PRINCE REGENT (FOR THE LAST NINE YEARS OF HIS FATHER'S REIGN) GEORGE BUILT THE ROYAL PAVILION IN BRIGHTON STARTING THE FASHION FOR SEASIDE RESORTS.

GILRAY'S CARTOONS MOCKED THE DEBAUCHED KING.

LOUIS BRAILLE DEVELOPED A SYSTEM OF RAISED DOTS ENABLING BLIND PEOPLE TO READ.

MARIA FITZHERBERT WAS A CATHOLIC WIDOW. HER MARRIAGE TO GEORGE WAS CONSIDERED INVALID AS IT WAS AGAINST THE LAW FOR A CATHOLIC TO BECOME QUEEN.

IN 1829 THE METROPOLITAN POLICE FORCE WAS FOUNDED BY ROBERT PEEL. POLICEMEN WERE NICKNAMED 'PEELERS' OR 'BOBBIES' AFTER HIS NAME.

GEORGE'S SECOND MARRIAGE, TO CAROLINE, WAS NOT A SUCCESS. THEY LIVED APART FOR YEARS. WHEN HE WAS ABOUT TO BE CROWNED KING SHE RETURNED FROM HER HOME IN ITALY TO BECOME QUEEN. GEORGE WOULDN'T ALLOW IT AND BANNED HER FROM THE CORONATION CEREMONY.

NAPOLEON BONAPARTE

THE DUKE OF WELLINGTON

TREATED AS A HERO AFTER HE DEFEATED NAPOLEON, THE DUKE OF WELLINGTON BECAME PRIME MINISTER IN 1828.

CAROLINE OF BRUNSWICK

STEPHENSON'S 'ROCKET' REACHED A TOP SPEED OF 3 MPH. BRITAIN'S FIRST PUBLIC RAILWAY LINE FROM STOCKTON TO DARLINGTON WAS OPENED IN 1825.

FLUSH LAVATORIES CAME INTO USE.

EXILED TO ST. HELENA BY THE BRITISH, NAPOLEON DIED OF BOREDOM AND ILL-HEALTH IN 1821.

THE WELLINGTON BOOT WAS NAMED AFTER HIM.

IN 1823 CHARLES MACINTOSH PATENTED A WATERPROOF FABRIC & OPENED A FACTORY TO MANUFACTURE MACINTOSHES!

BORN 1762 SUCCEEDED 1820 MARRIED MARIA FITZHERBERT & CAROLINE DIED 1830 BURIED AT WINDSOR

WILLIAM IV

HAD NO HEIR of HIS OWN

KNOWN AS THE SAILOR KING, WASHINGTON IRVING SAID OF HIM, 'HIS MAJESTY HAS AN EASY AND NATURAL WAY OF WIPING HIS NOSE WITH THE BACK OF HIS FOREFINGER WHICH I FANCY IS A RELIC OF HIS MIDDY (MIDSHIPMAN) HABITS!' IRVING WAS THE AUTHOR OF 'RIP VAN WINKLE' AND 'THE LEGEND OF SLEEPY HOLLOW'.

TIGHT CORSETS WERE THE FASHION FOR LADIES.

IN 1832 THE GREAT REFORM BILL WAS PASSED AFTER MUCH PROTESTING FROM THE HOUSE OF LORDS. THIS INCREASED THE NUMBER OF PEOPLE ALLOWED TO VOTE IN ELECTIONS BY ABOUT 50%. ALTHOUGH THE NEW INDUSTRIALISTS NOW GOT THE VOTE, NEITHER WORKING MEN OR WOMEN QUALIFIED.

IN 1833 SIX FARM LABOURERS FROM TOLPUDDLE IN DORSET FOUNDED A FRIENDLY SOCIETY TO SECURE A REASONABLE WAGE FOR ITS MEMBERS. LOCAL MAGISTRATES ARRESTED THE MEN AND EVEN THOUGH TRADE UNIONS HAD BEEN MADE LEGAL IN 1824, THE TOLPUDDLE MARTYRS WERE TRANSPORTED TO AUSTRALIA.

QUEEN ADELAIDE

WILLIAM SERVED IN THE NAVY FROM THE AGE OF 13 AND BECAME ADMIRAL OF THE FLEET IN 1811.

AS GEORGE III's 3rd SON, WILLIAM NEVER EXPECTED TO BECOME KING, BUT HE BECAME NEXT IN LINE WHEN HIS OLDER BROTHER, THE DUKE OF YORK, DIED IN 1827.

CHARLES DICKENS ACHIEVED GREAT SUCCESS WITH HIS FIRST NOVEL 'THE PICKWICK PAPERS' AT THE AGE OF 24. HE WENT ON TO WRITE MANY MORE. HIS PERSONAL FAVOURITE WAS 'DAVID COPPERFIELD'.

THE BRONTË SISTERS

ANNE EMILY CHARLOTTE

ALL THREE SISTERS HAD BOOKS PUBLISHED, THE MOST NOTABLE BEING EMILY'S 'WUTHERING HEIGHTS' & CHARLOTTE'S 'JANE EYRE'. THEY LIVED IN HAWORTH ON THE YORKSHIRE MOORS, DAUGHTERS OF A PARSON, WITH THEIR BROTHER, BRANWELL.

WILLIAM WILBERFORCE WORKED FOR 40 YEARS TO ABOLISH SLAVERY AND FINALLY ACHIEVED HIS AIM IN 1833 WHEN IT WAS ABOLISHED THROUGHOUT THE EMPIRE.

BORN 1765 SUCCEEDED 1830 MARRIED ADELAIDE of SAXE-MEININGEN DIED 1837 BURIED AT WINDSOR

SO GOOD QUEEN VICTORIA CAME TO THE THRONE

CRINOLINES, CAGES MADE FROM WHALE BONE, WERE WORN UNDER DRESSES TO HELP THEM IN THE FASHIONABLE BELL SHAPE. THEY WERE HEAVY AND OFTEN ROSE UP WHEN LADIES SAT DOWN! TO OVERCOME THESE DIFFICULTIES, INFLATABLE RUBBER CRINOLINES WERE INVENTED, BUT THESE TENDED TO PUNCTURE!

THE QUEEN & HER CONSORT HAD 9 CHILDREN AND WERE A DEVOTED COUPLE.

WHEN ALBERT DIED, AGED JUST 42, THE QUEEN WAS INCONSOLABLE FOR ALMOST 10 YEARS.

ALBERT INTRODUCED CHRISTMAS TREES TO BRITAIN.

ALBERT HAD THE IDEA OF A 'GREAT EXHIBITION' AT THE CRYSTAL PALACE TO SHOW BRITAIN'S SCIENTIFIC AND INDUSTRIAL SUPREMACY.

PRINCE ALBERT

THE BRITISH COMMONWEALTH BY THE END OF VICTORIA'S REIGN ONE-FIFTH OF THE WORLD WAS UNDER BRITISH CONTROL.

THOMAS EDDISON INVENTED THE LIGHTBULB IN 1899.

VICTORIA'S FOOTPRINT CAN BE SEEN ON THE STEPS OF ST MICHAEL'S MOUNT, CORNWALL.

DISRAELI WAS VICTORIA'S FAVOURITE PRIME MINISTER. WHEN HE DIED, THE QUEEN HAD A MONUMENT ERECTED IN THE CHURCH NEAR HIS HOME OF HUGHENDEN MANOR, BUCKINGHAMSHIRE.

LEVI STRAUSS MADE THE FIRST JEANS IN 1874.

THE BRILLIANT AND VERSATILE ENGINEER, BRUNEL, DESIGNED RAILWAYS, BRIDGES & SHIPS INCLUDING THE GREAT WESTERN, THE FIRST STEAMSHIP TO CROSS THE ATLANTIC.

KARL BENZ DEVELOPED THE FIRST PETROL-DRIVEN CAR IN 1885.

VICTORIA WAS WILLIAM IV'S NIECE. HER REIGN OF 64 YEARS MAKES HER BRITAIN'S LONGEST REIGNING MONARCH.

ALEXANDER GRAHAM BELL INVENTED THE TELEPHONE IN 1876 AND MARCONI INVENTED THE WIRELESS NEARLY 20 YEARS LATER IN 1895.

THE PENNY BLACK THE FIRST POSTAGE STAMP

ONE PENNY

CALLED THE LADY OF THE LAMP BECAUSE SHE CARRIED A LANTERN ON HER ROUNDS DURING THE CRIMEAN WAR, FLORENCE WAS THE PIONEER OF NURSING IN HOSPITALS.

FLORENCE NIGHTINGALE

ISAMBARD KINGDOM BRUNEL

BORN 1819 SUCCEEDED 1837 MARRIED ALBERT PRINCE OF SAXE-COBURG-GOTHA DIED 1901 BURIED AT FROGMORE, WINDSOR

EDWARD VII

LOVED GAMBLING AND FUN

EDWARD CHARMED THE LADIES & WAS CALLED TUM-TUM BECAUSE OF HIS SIZE.

A KEEN BETTING MAN, HE MADE £415,840 FROM HORSERACING IN THE LAST 24 YEARS OF HIS LIFE.

EMMELINE PANKHURST

QUEEN ALEXANDRA

IN 1903 THE WOMEN'S SOCIAL & POLITICAL UNION WAS SET UP BY EMMELINE & CHRISTABEL PANKHURST TO CAMPAIGN FOR VOTES FOR WOMEN.

DAUGHTER OF CHRISTIAN IX OF DENMARK, SHE WAS A BEAUTIFUL AND POPULAR QUEEN & MUCH LOVED BY HER CHILDREN. SLIGHTLY DEAF, HER HEARING WORSENED IN LATER LIFE. THE QUEEN ALSO HAD A LIMP, WHICH LADIES COPIED, CALLING IT THE ALEXANDRA GLIDE.

THE WRIGHT BROTHERS MADE THE FIRST AEROPLANE FLIGHT IN 1903.

TEDDY BEARS WERE NAMED AFTER THEODORE ROOSEVELT, THE AMERICAN PRESIDENT, WHO REFUSED TO SHOOT A BEAR WHILST OUT HUNTING.

SARAH BERNHARDT

EDWARD HAD MANY MISTRESSES, THE MOST FAMOUS BEING THE ACTRESSES LILY LANGTRY & SARAH BERNHARDT

LILY LANGTRY

BORN 1841 SUCCEEDED 1901 MARRIED ALEXANDRA of DENMARK DIED 1910 BURIED AT WINDSOR

GEORGE V REIGNED THROUGH WORLD WAR I

1914 to 1918 THE FIRST WORLD WAR

WHEN GERMANY INVADED BELGIUM IN 1914, BRITAIN AGREED TO JOIN THE WAR AGAINST THE CONTINENTAL POWERS (GERMANY, AUSTRIA, HUNGARY AND TURKEY). THE ALLIES - FRANCE, BRITAIN AND RUSSIA - FINALLY DEFEATED THE ENEMY BUT OVER 17 MILLION PEOPLE DIED IN TOTAL.

MICKEY MOUSE WAS CREATED BY WALT DISNEY IN 1928.

DOCTORS WERE CONCERNED THAT DANCING THE CHARLESTON MIGHT CAUSE PROBLEMS WITH CHILDBIRTH! ANOTHER FASHION CRAZE WAS THE 'HOBBLE SKIRT'

ALSO APTLY NAMED WERE 'OXFORD BAGS', TROUSERS WORN BY YOUNG MEN OF FASHION.

GEORGE WAS ANOTHER KING WHO NEVER EXPECTED TO WEAR THE CROWN. A NAVAL OFFICER, HE BECAME THE HEIR WHEN HIS ELDER BROTHER, EDWARD, DIED UNEXPECTEDLY.

BRITONS YOU

A FAMOUS RECRUITMENT POSTER SHOWING LORD KITCHENER TELLING YOUNG MEN TO JOIN THE ARMED FORCES.

WILLIAM II THE KAISER

KNOWN AS 'KAISER BILL' WAS GERMANY'S COMMANDER-IN-CHIEF.

LAWRENCE OF ARABIA
A ROMANTIC HERO OF THE WAR T.E. LAWRENCE HELPED TO UNITE THE ARAB TRIBES. HE WROTE 'THE SEVEN PILLARS OF WISDOM' ABOUT HIS EXPERIENCES

WHEN EDWARD VII DIED, GEORGE WROTE 'I HAVE LOST MY BEST FRIEND & THE BEST OF FATHERS. I NEVER HAD A (CROSS) WORD WITH HIM IN MY LIFE!'

IN 1919 WOMEN OVER 30 WERE GIVEN THE VOTE. IT TOOK ANOTHER 9 YEARS BEFORE WOMEN OVER 21 COULD VOTE.

QUEEN MARY

THE BBC STARTED RADIO BROADCASTS IN 1922 TELEVISION WAS INVENTED IN 1926 BY JOHN L BAIRD

PRINCESS MAY CHANGED HER NAME TO 'MARY' WHEN SHE BECAME QUEEN. SHE WAS RATHER STERN AND THE COUPLE WERE SOMETIMES REFERRED TO AS 'GEORGE & THE DRAGON.'

IN 1912 THE TITANIC SANK AFTER HITTING AN ICEBERG ON ITS MAIDEN VOYAGE. 1533 PEOPLE DIED. THE LINER WAS THOUGHT TO BE UNSINKABLE.

BORN 1865 SUCCEEDED 1910 MARRIED MAY of TECK DIED 1936 BURIED AT WINDSOR

EDWARD VIII GAVE THE THRONE FOR A WIFE

EDWARD CHOSE TO MARRY WALLIS SIMPSON, A TWICE DIVORCED AMERICAN, BUT THE GOVERNMENT AND THE COUNTRY WOULD NOT ACCEPT HER AS QUEEN SO EDWARD ABDICATED.

THEY LIVED IN SELF-IMPOSED EXILE IN FRANCE EXCEPT DURING THE SECOND WORLD WAR WHEN EDWARD WAS GOVERNOR OF THE BAHAMAS.

BORN 1894 SUCCEEDED 1936
MARRIED MRS SIMPSON ABDICATED 1936
DIED 1972 BURIED AT WINDSOR

GEORGE VI SAW MORE WORLD WAR STRIFE

ALTHOUGH DOMINATED BY THE WAR YEARS, GEORGE'S REIGN HAD A LIGHTER SIDE. BRITAIN HOSTED THE OLYMPIC GAMES IN 1948 & THE FESTIVAL OF BRITAIN CELEBRATED BRITISH ART AND DESIGN IN 1951.

THE BEANO WAS FIRST PUBLISHED IN 1938.

IN MANCHESTER THE FIRST ELECTRONIC COMPUTOR, THE MARK I, WAS BUILT IN 1948.

GEORGE WAS KNOWN AS 'BERTIE' TO HIS FAMILY.

ELIZABETH BOWES-LYON

THE 2ND WORLD WAR 1939 TO 1945

WHEN GERMANY, UNDER THE NAZI PARTY, INVADED POLAND IN 1939, BRITAIN DECLARED WAR ON GERMANY. ITALY AND JAPAN JOINED FORCES WITH GERMANY. THE AMERICANS JOINED THE ALLIES AFTER THE JAPANESE BOMBED THEIR FLEET AT PEARL HARBOR IN 1941. BOMBING THROUGHOUT THE WAR KILLED NEARLY 100,000 CIVILIANS, WHILE OVER A QUARTER OF A MILLION SERVICEMEN WERE KILLED. THE NAZIS MURDERED MILLIONS OF JEWS IN WHAT IS KNOWN AS THE 'HOLOCAUST'.

ADOLF HITLER

WINSTON CHURCHILL

BRITAIN'S LEADER THROUGHOUT THE WAR, CHURCHILL WAS PRIME MINISTER TWICE & SAT IN PARLIAMENT FOR OVER 47 YEARS.

BORN 1895 SUCCEEDED 1936
MARRIED ELIZABETH BOWES-LYON
DIED 1952 BURIED AT WINDSOR

ELIZABETH II WAS CROWNED YOUNG & SERENE AND THE PEOPLE STILL SING GOD SAVE OUR QUEEN

ELIZABETH'S CORONATION WAS THE FIRST TO BE TELEVISED. COMMERCIAL TELEVISION STARTED IN 1955 AND THE FIRST ADVERTISEMENT WAS FOR TOOTHPASTE.

THE 'SPACE RACE': THE FORMER USSR WAS THE FIRST TO ACHIEVE SPACE TRAVEL LAUNCHING SPUTNIK I IN 1957 BUT... AMERICA'S ASTRONAUTS NEIL ARMSTRONG AND BUZZ ALDRIN WERE THE FIRST MEN ON THE MOON.

COLOUR TELEVISION WAS FIRST BROADCAST ON BBC 2 IN 1966.

BRITAIN & FRANCE BUILT CONCORDE, AN AEROPLANE THAT CAN FLY FASTER THAN THE SPEED OF SOUND. ANOTHER JOINT VENTURE, THE CHANNEL TUNNEL OPENED TO THE PUBLIC IN 1994.

IN 1954 ROGER BANNISTER BECAME THE FIRST MAN TO RUN THE MILE IN UNDER 4 MINUTES.

IN 1972 THE CURRENCY WAS DECIMALIZED. BEFORE THAT POUNDS SHILLINGS AND PENCE WERE USED. THERE WERE 12 PENNIES IN A SHILLING AND 20 SHILLINGS IN A POUND.

SIR EDWARD HEATH

SIR EDWARD HEATH WAS THE PRIME MINISTER WHO LEAD BRITAIN INTO THE EUROPEAN COMMUNITY IN 1973.

MARGARET THATCHER

IN 1982 THE MARY ROSE, HENRY VIII'S FLAGSHIP, WAS RAISED AND PUT ON SHOW IN PORTSMOUTH. IT HAD BEEN ON THE SEA BED FOR OVER 450 YEARS.

BETTY BOOTHROYD WAS THE FIRST WOMAN TO BECOME 'SPEAKER' IN THE HOUSE OF COMMONS.

BRITAIN'S FIRST WOMAN PRIME MINISTER.

BORN 1926 SUCCEEDED 1952 MARRIED PHILIP MOUNTBATTEN